TAKE THE LEAD

TENOR SAXOPHONE

Musicals

Series Editor: Anna Joyce

Editorial, production and recording: Artemis Music Limited • Design and production: Space DPS Limited • Published 2001

IMP

International MUSIC Publications

Fame
from *Fame*

Words by Dean Pitchford
Music by Michael Gore

Bright pop feel

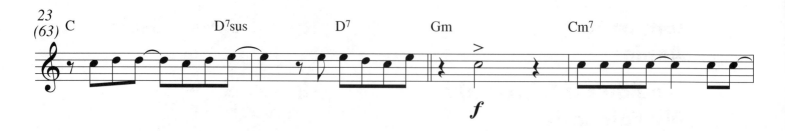

Demonstration

Backing

Food Glorious Food
from *Oliver*

Words and Music by Lionel Bart

Demonstration   Backing

If I Were A Rich Man

from *Fiddler On The Roof*

Words by Sheldon Harnick
Music by Jerry Bock

Demonstration Backing

Over The Rainbow
from *The Wizard Of Oz*

Words by E Y Harburg
Music by Harold Arlen

Ballad tempo

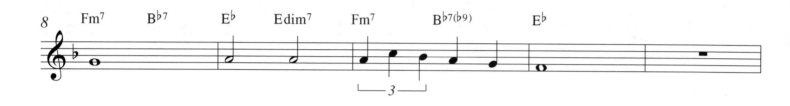

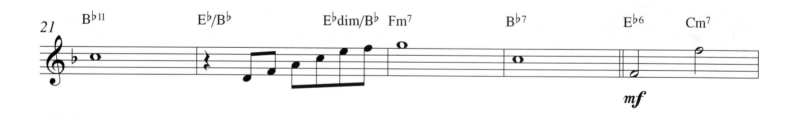

Send In The Clowns
from *A Little Night Music*

Demonstration   Backing

Words and Music by
Stephen Sondheim

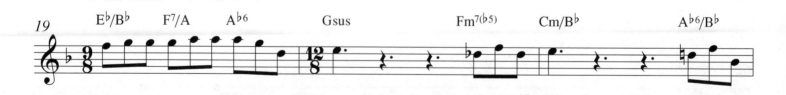

Demonstration   Backing

Singin' In The Rain
from *Singin' In The Rain*

Words by Arthur Freed
Music by Nacio Herb Brown

Tomorrow
from *Annie*

Words by Martin Charnin
Music by Charles Strouse

Demonstration   Backing

Wouldn't It Be Loverly
from *My Fair Lady*

Words by Alan Jay Lerner
Music by Frederick Loewe

Printed by Halstan & Co. Ltd., Amersham, Bucks., England